CLAIRE:
JUSTICE
NINJA

JOE BRADY

KATE ASHWIN

Writing: Joe Brady
Art: Kate Ashwin
Additional Colours: Lisa Murphy

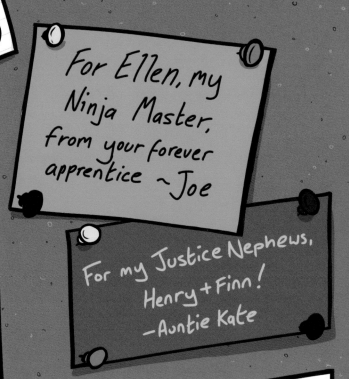

For Ellen, my Ninja Master, from your forever apprentice ~Joe

For my Justice Nephews, Henry + Finn! —Auntie Kate

Claire: Justice Ninja
is a
DAVID FICKLING BOOK

First published in
Great Britain in 2019 by
David Fickling Books,
31 Beaumont Street,
Oxford, OX1 2NP

Text © Joe Brady, 2019
Illustrations
© Kate Ashwin, 2019

978-1-78845-100-0
13 5 7 9 10 8 6 4 2

Papers used by David Fickling Books are from well-managed forests and other responsible sources.

DAVID FICKLING BOOKS Reg. No. 8340307

A CIP catalogue record for this book is available from the British Library.

Printed and bound in Great Britain by Sterling.

OPERATION
(35) OVERDUE JUSTICE

So many late library books!

VRRM!

Litter!

OPERATION
(39) IN THE BIN

SEWER

MR. COX
(LOUD BIKE)

rory

(43) **OPERATION**
TOO LOUD TO BE ALLOWED!

Really LOUD bike !!

Play Fair!

OPERATION
(49)
GAME SHAME

Nigel's Business Papers

OPERATION (53)
FEE to WEE

30p CHARGE

30p to use the loo?!

first years

NO bullies allowed!

OPERATION (57)
STAND UP AND BAND UP

tHANK

OPERATION CAR PARK SHARK!

Corrupt Politician

I CAN'T BELIEVE THE LOCAL COUNCIL HAS DECIDED TO TURN THE PLAYGROUND INTO A CAR PARK!

CARS DON'T NEED PARKS, KIDS NEED PARKS!

YEAH, BUT...

...THE COUNCIL HAS ALL THE POWER!

SO WHAT CAN WE DO?

WE CAN DO WHAT WE ALWAYS DO.

DISGUISED AS *MYSELF*...

I, *CLAIRE,* JUSTICE NINJA: NINJA OF JUSTICE...

WILL BRING JUSTICE TO *SELF-SERVING* LOCAL OFFICIALS!

COUNCILLOR MACKABEE

LOVES- MONEY CARS
HATES- KIDS

THE HEAD OF THE COUNCIL WANTS A CAR PARK.

HIS EVIL PLAN TO GET IT IS SIMPLE.

PHASE ONE: HE TAKES OVER THE PLAYGROUND.

PHASE TWO: HE DESTROYS SAID PLAYGROUND.

PHASE THREE: HE TURNS IT INTO A PARK FOR CARS.

A-ALL RIGHT, EXCEPT ONE THING...

THIS IS THE HEAD OF THE LOCAL COUNCIL! THE *LOCAL COUNCIL!* WE CAN'T STOP HIM!

EXACTLY. HE WANTS A CAR PARK...

SO THAT'S *EXACTLY* WHAT HE'LL GET.

??? ???

HERE IT IS, THE LAIR OF COUNCILLOR MACKABEE.

WHAT ARE WE DOING HERE? IF THEY FIND OUT WE'RE HERE, THEY'LL...

RELAX, MY APPRENTICE, HE WON'T FIND US.

HE'S TOO BUSY ENJOYING *THE SPOILS OF CORRUPTION.*

GASP!

££££££££!

ALL RIGHT. HOW DO WE TAKE THIS CORRUPT JERK DOWN?

WITH ONE MINOR ACT OF FULLY JUSTIFIED ROBBERY...

KEEP OUT
CONSTRUCTION

KERRRASSHH!

LET'S GET PAVING!

KEEP OUT CONSTRUCTION

THE NEXT MORNING...

yaaaawn!

heh heh.

DAILY NOOS
NEW CAR PARK OPENS TODAY!

VROOOOM!!!

SLAM!

CAR PARK

NEWS

yay!

Woo!

THANK YOU FOR LISTENING TO US, COUNCILLOR.

USING YOUR OWN LAND INSTEAD OF THE CHILDREN'S RECREATION AREA FOR THE CAR PARK IS SUCH A *GENEROUS* GESTURE!

NEWS

YES... WELL...

GRUMBLE GRUMBLE.

ANYTHING FOR THOSE BEAUTIFUL CHILDREN.

EXCELLENT WORK, MY APPRENTICE! WE HAVE UNDONE A GRAVE INJUSTICE.

PHEW!

CAR PARK

NOW, IF I COULD ONLY FIND A PLACE TO LEAVE THIS THING. PARKING AROUND HERE IS RIDICULOUS!

JUSTICE SERVED

OPERATION BUBBLE GLUM

Spitting gum on the ground

DISGUISED AS *MYSELF*...

I, *CLAIRE*, JUSTICE NINJA: NINJA OF JUSTICE...

STREEETCH!

SQUISH!

WILL BRING JUSTICE TO THE *GUM SPITTER!*

NIGEL, I NEED YOU.

the PHOENIX

the PHOENIX

WE HAVE A NEW MISSION.

NICE! GUM!

OH, MY HAPLESS APPRENTICE.

THIS IS NOT GUM *FOR* THE *MOUTH.*

IT'S GUM *FROM* THE *GROUND.*

ERGH!

SPEWED FROM THE MOUTH OF THAT *GUM-SPITTER,* MARCY MAPLETHORPE.

THAT'S PRETTY GROSS, CLAIRE! MY COUSIN GOT REALLY SICK AFTER HE CHEWED GUM OFF THE GROUND.

GASP!

WHAT IS IT?

QUICK! GIVE ME YOUR TELESCOPE!

ENJOY IT WHILE IT LASTS, MARCY MAPLETHORPE.

Ptoo!

BECAUSE YOU'VE JUST MADE YOURSELF A POWERFUL ENEMY.

WHAT'S THE MOVE, JUSTICE NINJA?

FOR CRYING OUT LOUD!

NOW, WE WAIT.

THAT'S NOT RIGHT...

WHO'S THE TARGET AGAIN?!

ERK!

ew!

GOT HER.

WHAT THE...?

CHEW CHEW CHEW

HONESTLY, *WHO* JUST LEAVES THEIR GUM ON THE *STREET*?!

IT LOOKS LIKE MAYBE WE GOT A FEW PEOPLE WHO DIDN'T DESERVE IT...

SOMETIMES THAT'S WHAT IT TAKES.

WAAAAAH!

hop!

dagnabit?!

pto!

MIRROOW!

CAN YOU SMELL THAT? THAT'S THE SMELL OF JUSTICE.

Snff

WHY DOES JUSTICE SMELL LIKE *SPILT* MILK?

THE *MILK!*

whew!

CLAIRE! WHERE'S MY MILK?!

COMING, MUM!

JUSTICE SERVED

OPERATION
~ BIRTHDAY RIFT ~

Buys rubbish gifts

...Y **BIIIRTHDAY** dear Nigel..... **MYOOOW!** **HAAAAPPY** birthday to **YOOOOU!**

OH, A TURTLE HAT! ISN'T THAT, ER... LOVELY, NIGEL!

I JUST KNOW HOW MUCH YOU LOVE TURTLES!

THANKS, AUNTIE GEMMA...!

selfie!

I'M THE COOL AUNT

I THOUGHT YOU **LOVED** TURTLES, APPRENTICE.

I DID LOVE TURTLES, WHEN I WAS A LITTLE **KID.**

...BUT I WISH PEOPLE WOULD **STOP** GETTING ME TURTLE STUFF!

The B?? Book of Turtles

THEN PERHAPS IT'S TIME WE GAVE **THEM** A GIFT.

I MEAN, **SURE**, THEY WERE AROUND AT THE SAME TIME AS DINOSAURS, HAVE GLANDS THAT FILTER SALT FROM OCEAN WATER AND SOME SPECIES CAN BURP.

THE GIFT OF **JUSTICE!**

NO.

PLEASE.

THIS IS MY FAMILY BIRTHDAY PARTY...!

DISGUISED AS *MYSELF*...

I, *CLAIRE*, JUSTICE NINJA: NINJA OF JUSTICE...

swssh!

WILL BRING JUSTICE TO *NIGEL'S FAMILY BIRTHDAY PARTY!*

WHAT ARE YOU DOING IN HERE?

I'M DOING RESEARCH ON THE *ENEMY*.

IS THAT AUNTIE GEMMA'S PHONE?!

STUDYING HER *WEAKNESSES*. LEARNING ABOUT HER *FRAILTIES*.

FINDING WAYS TO TEACH HER WHAT IT'S LIKE TO BE SPAMMED WITH TAT YOU NEITHER NEED NOR WANT.

WHICH MEANS...?

AUNTIE GEMMA SHOULD *NOT* HAVE INSTALLED THE 'ONE CLICK PURCHASE' APP.

SHE WILL RECEIVE *8 PAIRS* OF MEN'S HIKING BOOTS, A *MILE* OF STRING, *A PINT* OF OWL VOMIT AND *THREE* OF FOX WEE, A *"TAXIDERMY YOUR PETS"* KIT, *75 KILOS* OF A CHEESE KNOWN AS "STINKING BISHOP", AND A WIG, MADE SPECIALLY TO FIT ON THE SOFT HEAD OF A *BABY*.

ULTRA

EXPRESS

DELIVERY.

OKAY...? WELL, IN THE MEANTIME, EVERYONE IS LEAVING AND AUNTIE GEMMA IS GOING *CRAZY* LOOKING FOR HER PHONE.

ADDED TO BILL

WITH EXTRA MUD

1M (MILE, NOT METRE)

FROM QUALITY OWL

DO NOT DRINK!

NOT FOR USE ON LIVE PETS

ACTUAL SIZE

FOR VERY STYLISH BABIES

ka-CHING!

YOU GEMMA?

SIGN HERE.

FOR **ALL** OF THESE?!

AND ALL OF THAT.

FOX **WEE**?! WHY WOULD I WANT **FOX WEE**?

IF YOU DIDN'T WANT IT, WHY DID YOU ORDER IT?

AND THAT'S HOW JUSTICE IS SERVED.

YOU KNOW, I ACTUALLY REALLY LIKE FAMILY BIRTHDAY PARTIES!

YEAH, THEY'RE NOT SO BAD.

WELL, HAPPY BIRTHDAY, APPRENTICE. CHECK YOU TOMORROW.

WAIT A MINUTE...

NOT THAT IT MATTERS...

BUT YOU DIDN'T GET ME ANYTHING.

UM... MASTERS DON'T GET THEIR APPRENTICES PRESENTS.

DON'T BE GREEDY.

THEN WHAT'S *THIS?*

IT'S NOT A BIG DEAL, MY MUM PICKED IT OUT!

RAAIPP?!

hahaha

hahahaha

YOU KNOW WHAT JUSTICE NINJAS DO TO PEOPLE WHO AREN'T GRATEFUL?!

THANKYOUCLAIRE ILOVEMYPRESENT!

GOOD!

Pfchh..!

TURTLEY RAD

JUSTICE SERVED

NIGEL'S TIPS!

STRETCHES

of Justice!

LEG STRETCHES
for running away from angry butchers

ARM STRETCHES
for carrying ninja disguises

TOE STRETCHES
for sneaking on roof tops

EAR STRETCHES
for listening to the call of JUSTICE!

JAW STRETCHES
for gum chewing

MIND STRETCHES
for doing everything your ninja master says

STRETCH EVERYTHING

all the time, because an apprentice must be ready for everything. ALL THE TIME.

NIGEL'S TOP TIPS!

My foolproof thank you note formula!

present **Dear** _____Claire_____, ← Person's name

Thank you for the
_____Turtley rad T-shirt_____,
**I really like it! It was
great to see you at the**
birthday party, **I hope to see
you again soon!**

↑ Where you saw them

**Love,
Nigel!** Add a bit here + there to make it personal

Remember to put your name and not 'Nigel' though! Unless Nigel is your name too, in which case: hello, fellow Nigel!

OPERATION HAM SCAMWICH

The Worst Bully!

CHILDREN, GATHER ROUND!

IN ALL MY YEARS, I HAVE NEVER SEEN SUCH DISREGARD FOR SCHOOL PROPERTY!

I... I FOUND...

...A HAM SANDWICH IN A LIBRARY BOOK!

HAHAHAHAHA!

Eww!

eurgh! HA HAA HA!

THIS IS NOT FUNNY. BOOKS ARE OUR FRIENDS...

YES, CLAIRE?

MRS WINKLE, MAY I GO TO THE TOILET?

WHAM!

BOOKS ARE OUR FRIENDS.

GIRLS

OUR FRIENDS MUST BE DEFENDED.

DISGUISED AS *MYSELF*...

I, *CLAIRE*, JUSTICE NINJA: NINJA OF JUSTICE...

WILL BRING *JUSTICE* TO THE *SANDWICH SQUASHER!*

OOH, I LOVE HAM SANDWICHES!

AH! YOU'RE NOT ALLOWED IN HERE!

A FEW MOMENTS LATER.

HERE'S THE PLAN.

WE'RE NOT SUPPOSED TO BE BACK HERE.

I JUST NEED TO HACK INTO THE SYSTEM SO I CAN DISCOVER WHO CHECKED THAT BOOK OUT LAST.

tap *tap tap*

School Rec...

HORACE MINEFIELD

I *KNEW* IT. THE BIGGEST JERK IN THE SCHOOL...

...to bully other, smaller children

HORACE MINEFIELD.

HOW WAS SCHOOL, MY PRINCE?

SCHOOL BORES ME.

22

SNZZZZz

CLAIRE, WAKE UP!

WHAT IS IT?!

H-YAH!

I DON'T THINK THE PLAN QUITE WORKED OUT...

WHAT?!

NO TRESPASSERS

HAM SANDWICHES
For sale

IMPOSSIBLE!

KA-CHING!

IN FAILURE, THE NINJA ALWAYS FINDS A LESSON. THE LESSON TODAY IS...

NIGEL?

WHAT ABOUT THIS FOR A LESSON: "WHEN LIFE GIVES YOU A HAM SANDWICH, TAKE A BITE!"

CHOMP!

AN EXCELLENT LESSON, MY APPRENTICE.

Blergh!

ESPECIALLY BECAUSE I OVERLOADED THE MAYO WITH LAXATIVES.

JUSTICE SERVED

OPERATION SLICE OF JUSTICE

Picking the Pepperoni off!?!

I'M SO FULL!

ME TOO!

AHH! ZOMBIES! HELP US. NINJA MASTER!

I COULDN'T EAT ANOTHER BITE.

CHOMP.

ISN'T FAMILY MOVIE NIGHT FUN?

SHH!

SO MUCH _FUN_.

I'M GOING 'TO THE TOILET'.

AND BY 'TO THE TOILET' I MEAN I'M GOING TO SHOW YOU TO _NEVER_ PICK THE TOPPINGS OFF THE PIZZA EVER AGAIN!

SCREECH!

shh!

chomp.

DISGUISED AS *MYSELF*...

I, *CLAIRE*, JUSTICE NINJA: NINJA OF JUSTICE...

WILL BRING JUSTICE TO *MOVIE AND PIZZA NIGHT!*

CLACK

ON!

heh.

YOUR RESPONSE TIME TO THE NIGEL SIGNAL *DISAPPOINTS* ME, APPRENTICE.

I WAS HAVING DINNER WITH MY NAN! IS EVERYTHING OKAY?

FOR ME, YES. BUT NOT FOR THE *PIZZA*. A GRAVE INJUSTICE HAS BEEN DONE TO MY CHEESY FRIEND!

SO, YOUR MUM PICKED OFF ALL THE TOPPINGS AGAIN?

BUT IF YOU WEREN'T GOING TO HAVE ANOTHER PIECE, THEN—

EVER HEAR OF LEFTOVERS?!

COLD PIZZA IS SUPERIOR TO *FRESH* PIZZA IN MANY WAYS...

NOT IF THE TOPPINGS HAVE BEEN REMOVED, THEN IT'S JUST *SOGGY BREAD-CHEESE!*

BUT YOUR MUM PAID FOR THE PIZZA...

WHAT ARE YOU, AN APPRENTICE JUSTICE NINJA, OR AN APOLOGIST FOR INJUSTICE?!

I CAN'T BELIEVE YOUR MUM WOULD DO SOMETHING SO HORRIBLE.

MUM WILL WANT CHOCOLATE-CHIP COOKIES AND COOKIE-DOUGH ICE CREAM NOW. SHE ALWAYS DOES.

YOU KNOW WHAT TO DO.

27

OPERATION BUS STOP FLOP

Late bus **AGAIN!**

WHEN'S THE BUS GETTING HERE?!

LATE, AS *USUAL!*

§ SQUEEEP!

OH, HELLO, MR TOMLIN. NICE DAY TO HAVE A *LEISURELY* DRIVE AROUND THE NEIGHBOURHOOD, EH?

OH, CLAIRE, YOU CRACK ME UP!

OH, I *CRACK YOU UP*, DO I? I'LL CRACK YOU UP! LIKE A *NUT!* IN A *CRACKER!*

A *NUT CRACKER!*

DISGUISED AS *MYSELF*...

I, *CLAIRE*, JUSTICE NINJA: NINJA OF JUSTICE...

WILL BRING JUSTICE TO THE *LOCAL BUS SYSTEM!*

I DON'T EVEN KNOW WHY I HOLD ON TO THE BUS TIMETABLE! IT'S NOT LIKE *ANY* BUS IS *EVER* ON TIME.

BUT WHAT CAN YOU DO ABOUT IT? SURELY INTERFERING WILL ONLY MAKE THE BUS EVEN *LATER.*

YOU CAN ALWAYS RIDE ON THE BACK OF MY BIKE WITH ME!

NO THANKS.

hmm...

GOOOAL!

whaaat?!

THAT'S *IT! THAT'S* WHAT I HAVE TO DO! KICK THAT BUS DRIVER INTO THE GOAL OF JUSTICE.

BUT FIRST, WE HAVE TO *STEAL HIS PERSONAL PLANNER.*

I'M IN!

OI!

Hey!

MY PLAN IS AS SIMPLE AS IT IS *PERFECT.*

THE BUS DRIVER *PAINSTAKINGLY* SCHEDULES EACH OF HIS PERSONAL APPOINTMENTS, MONTHS IN ADVANCE.

YOU'LL MAKE A NOISE TO DISTRACT HIM!

BANG!

No.1 Bus Driver

IS THAT YOU, NIGEL SIMONSON?! GET OUT OF MY BINS!

AND I'LL ALTER EACH ENTRY TO MAKE HIM SHOW UP *EARLY*, WHICH MEANS HE'LL THINK EVERYONE *ELSE* IS LATE...

AND THEN, WE WAIT.

AND WATCH?

OOOH, YES.

WE'RE *ALWAYS* WATCHING.

GP Reception

I'VE BEEN WAITING NEARLY AN HOUR!

MY DATE SAID SHE'D BE HERE HALF AN HOUR AGO...

I TELL YOU WHAT, IT IS NOT FUN TO BE KEPT WAITING.

I FEEL THE SAME WAY, MR TOMLIN.

MORNING, CLAIRE!

WHA..?

NO TRESPASSERS

IT'S GETTING LATE, SWEETIE.

I ❤ MY NINJA DAUGHTER

I....

...OVER-SLEPT?!

DAAAD!

WHY DIDN'T YOU WAKE ME UP EARLIER?!

SPORTS NEWS
FOOTBALL MAN KICKS THE BALL!
DAILY NEWS
LATE BUSES AGAIN!

I ❤ MY NINJA DAUGHTER

PFFH, LIKE THE BUS IS EVER ON TIME!

IT WILL BE TODAY!

BUS STOP

DAMMIT!

VROOM

HEY, CLAIRE!

BUS STOP

NEED A LIFT?

YOU CAN HOP ON MY BIKE IF YOU WANT!

THAT'S NOT WHAT I MEANT!

JUSTICE SERVED

Nigel's *tip top tips*

HAM SANDWICH
RECIPE OF Justice!

Ingredients: 2 slices of
Some ham   bread
         Glob of mayo

Step 1 : first, get bread!

Step 2 : Put mayo on bread!

Step 3 : Put ham on mayo!

Step 4 : Put other bread on ham!

and it's DAIRY FREE!

Nigel's biggest TOP tips

Guide to Disguises

The best disguises are ones of people who fit in everywhere. One type of person who fits in everywhere is A KID!

WEAR a shirt that a kid would wear!

WEAR shoes that a kid would wear!

HAVE a face that a kid would have!

BE an actual kid!!

Am I myself? Or am I just DISGUISED as myself?!

OPERATION OVERDUE JUSTICE

So many late library books!

STAMP! STAMP! STAMP

STAMP STAMP STOMP!

SHH!

OH, SORRY, CLAIRE. I WAS JUST LIBRARIAN-ISING...

STAMP!

OR WAS I?

NIGEL?! MY APPRENTICE?!

DON'T LET THE DISGUISE FOOL YOU. I'M NOT A LIBRARIAN. I'M HERE SCOPING OUT OPPORTUNITIES TO DOLE OUT *NINJA JUSTICE.*

WELL, I'M HERE TO READ. QUIETLY.

OH. SORRY. NEVER MIND THEN. I DIDN'T MEAN TO–

HOW EASILY YOU FALL PREY TO THE NINJA PERSUASION TRICK, MY APPRENTICE.

AND BY 'NINJA PERSUASION TRICK', YOU JUST MEAN *LYING*, RIGHT?

PRECISELY. I'M REALLY HERE BECAUSE... 3... 2...

1.

IT'S BEEN *WEEKS.* DO YOU HAVE ANY IDEA WHEN THE BOOK WILL BE BACK?

I DON'T, SORRY! PEOPLE JUST CHECK OUT BOOKS AND KEEP THEM.

I WISH *SOMEONE* WOULD DO *SOMETHING* ABOUT IT...

RETU

35

DISGUISED AS *MYSELF*...

I, *CLAIRE*, JUSTICE NINJA: NINJA OF *JUSTICE*...

WILL BRING *JUSTICE* TO PEOPLE WHO *DON'T RETURN* LIBRARY BOOKS!

AND *I'M* DISGUISED AS A LIBRARIAN!

SHHHHHH!

...CLAIRE? WHERE ARE YOU?

SO WHAT'S THE PLAN FOR JUSTICE, THEN?

MEET ME IN THAT ALLEY. I HAVE TWO THINGS TO TELL YOU.

ONE, YOU CALLED ME 'CLAIRE' IN PUBLIC. DON'T USE MY REAL NAME WHEN I'M IN DISGUISE AGAIN! MY ALTER EGO IS *CLAIRE*, MY REAL NAME IS *CLAIRE*. CAN YOU TELL THE DIFFERENCE?

NO.

EXACTLY.

AND *TWO*, EXCELLENT JOB!

YOU PROVIDED A DISTRACTION FOR ME TO STEAL THE ENTIRE LIST OF PEOPLE WITH OVERDUE LIBRARY BOOKS.

OVERDUE FEES

WHICH SETS THE STAGE FOR MY NEXT PLAN FOR *JUSTICE*.

SO WE'RE TAKING THE BOOKS BACK TO THE LIBRARY FOR EVERYONE, BUT HOW WILL THEY LEARN THEIR LESSON?

BECAUSE WE WON'T JUST RETURN LIBRARY BOOKS...

WE'LL RETURN ALL OF THE BOOKS!

THIS MORNING, ALL ACROSS THE NEIGHBOURHOOD, PEOPLE WILL WAKE TO FIND THEIR OWN BOOKS ARE MISSING.

THEY WILL THINK, WHAT IS GOING ON? WHO WOULD SIMPLY TAKE SOMETHING THAT DOES NOT BELONG TO THEM...

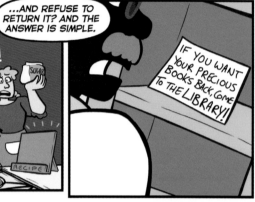

...AND REFUSE TO RETURN IT? AND THE ANSWER IS SIMPLE.

IF YOU WANT YOUR PRECIOUS BOOKS BACK, COME TO THE LIBRARY!

AND THAT'S HOW JUSTICE IS SERVED!

AHEM... TWO THINGS.

ONE, THAT'S MY LINE.

RETURNS

AND THAT'S HOW JUSTICE IS SERVED!

THEN WHAT'S THE SECOND THING?

DON'T PANDER TO STEREOTYPE, NIGEL. NOT ALL LIBRARIANS LOOK LIKE THAT.

JUSTICE SERVED

OPERATION IN THE BIN

VRRM!

Litter!

PLAY PARK

Pooof!

Whee!

Woo!

VRRM

IT'S A SLOW DAY FOR INJUSTICE, MY APPRENTICE.

HEY, WHAT'S THAT?

VRROOOM!

FIZZO

FLING!

GASP!

VRRM!

FIZZO

GET ME THE REGISTRATION NUMBER OF THAT CAR.

BOOT!

DISGUISED AS *MYSELF*...

I, *CLAIRE*, JUSTICE NINJA: NINJA OF JUSTICE...

WILL BRING JUSTICE TO THE *LITTERER!*

CLAIRE! CLAIRE!

YES, APPRENTICE?

I GOT HER REGISTRATION NUMBER!

SEEF

CLASSIC NIGEL. ALWAYS DOING WHAT YOU'RE TOLD.

I SENT YOU ON THAT POINTLESS ERRAND BECAUSE I NEEDED SOME AIR, MY APPRENTICE.

COO!

WAIT! THERE'S A *LESSON* HERE. YOU TELL ME TO DO WHAT I'M TOLD...

THEN WHEN I DO WHAT I'M TOLD, YOU TELL ME I SHOULDN'T HAVE DONE IT...

ARE YOU SAYING I GET TO START DISOBEYING YOU?!

GULP!

INCORRECT.

MEET ME IN THE BUNKER.

phew!

THE WOMAN IN THE CAR WAS GLORIA FINGERSTROP. SHE'S A NOTORIOUS LITTERER.

I DIDN'T NEED THE REG NUMBER BECAUSE I HAD ALREADY BEEN FOLLOWING HER FOR WEEKS.

HERE SHE IS LITTERING IN FRONT OF A BIN.

chomp!

HERE SHE IS LITTERING OUT OF HER WINDOW.

HERE SHE IS LITTERING IN FRONT OF A MONUMENT.

BURP

OR AT LEAST WHAT SHE *THOUGHT* WAS A MONUMENT.

I HAD TO SCRUB FOR HOURS TO GET THAT SILVER PAINT OFF ME.

AND IT WAS *ALL* WORTH IT.

3.6 AVERAGE LITTERS PER DAY
× 365.25 AVERAGE DAYS PER YEAR
× 81.6 AVERAGE YEARS PER LIFETIME

SHE LITTERS AN AVERAGE OF 3.6 TIMES A DAY.

LIFETIME LITTER EXPECTANCY.

107,295.8 PIECES OF LITTER

THAT'S A *LOT* OF LITTER.

107,295.8 SPLATS ON THE FACE OF MOTHER EARTH.

coo?

AND THAT'S *EXACTLY* WHAT FINGERSTROP WILL GET.

THE NEXT MORNING—

PLOPP!

OOO!

RUDDY PIGEONS!

AH, PIGEONS. NATURE'S LITTERERS.

AND *THAT'S* HOW JUSTICE IS SERVED.

COO!

DO YOU REALLY THINK SHE'S LEARNED HER LESSON?

I THINK SHE'S LEARNED *ONE* OF HER LESSONS.

JUST 107,294.8 MORE LESSONS TO GO!

COO!

I GUESS WE NEED TO GET YOU SOMETHING TO EAT.

JUSTICE SERVED

OPERATION
TOO LOUD TO BE ALLOWED!

Really LOUD bike !!

HEY, CLAIRE!

WHAT IS IT, MY APPRENTICE?

IT'S ABOUT THAT JUG, YOU KNOW...

VROOOOOMM

MR COX IS SO INCONSIDERATE!

YOU KNOW THE JUG I BORROWED FROM MY MUM FOR YOU?

VRROOOMM

THAT NOISE IS A NUISANCE TO THE NEIGHBOURHOOD, AND *JUSTICE* MUST BE SERVED.

IT'S JUST SHE'S ASKING ABOUT IT, AND—

CLAIRE?! ARE YOU EVEN LISTENING?

I HEAR *ALL*, MY APPRENTICE. ARE YOU COMING?

43

WHOSE TREE FORT IS THAT?

THE LOOKOUT OF JUSTICE.

UH, CLAIRE, PIGEON... *PIGEON!*

LEAVE HIM BE, RORY.

"COO.

COULD IT STILL BE IN THE LAB?

WHY ARE WE GOING INTO THE JUNKYARD?

WOOFWOOFWOOFWOOF!

KEEP OUT

YOU'RE BEING SUCH A TYPICAL APPRENTICE, MY APPRENTICE.

KEEP OUT

NINJA-CHEMISTRY LAB OF JUSTICE.

AH HAH!

THERE'S YOUR MUM'S JUG, BUT WE NEED TO EMPTY IT FIRST!

NOW, TO THE JUSTICE UNDERGROUND!

JUSTICE SERVED

NIGEL'S tippity tippest top TIPS!

Guide to disguises that are not Nigel

Librarian!

Chef!

Chicken!

THE NIGHT.

Pizza delivery boy!

OPERATION
GAME SHAME

Play Fair!

SAM? ARE YOU OKAY?

St. Martin's Primary School

NOT REALLY. MY DAD KEEPS PLAYING ON MY FANTASY SHOOTER ONLINE ACCOUNT. HE'S TERRIBLE!

I'M NEARLY AT THE TOP RANK, BUT EVERY TIME HE PLAYS, I DROP DOWN.

NO!

I'D PLAY WITH HIM, BUT HE SAYS HE DOESN'T HAVE TIME TO RANK UP HIS OWN CHARACTER.

THAT'S AWFUL!

KRAK!

CLAIRE! THE BELL'S ABOUT TO RING, SHOULDN'T WE GET TO LESSONS?

NOT TODAY, MY APPRENTICE. NOT TODAY.

IS THAT SAM'S DAD?

AND HE'S USING SAM'S GAME.

HAHA! ZAP!

POW!

HAHA!

Rank: DROPPED! SAMBONE72

-100!

WHOOPS! OH WELL, IT'S JUST A GAME!

WHY CAN'T HE JUST MAKE HIS OWN ACCOUNT?

LATE!

BECAUSE HE DOESN'T KNOW JUSTICE YET.

DISGUISED AS *MYSELF*...

I, *CLAIRE*, JUSTICE NINJA: NINJA OF JUSTICE...

WILL BRING JUSTICE FOR *SAM'S ONLINE AVATAR!*

FANTASY SHOOTER ONLINE. THE MOST POPULAR VIDEO GAME EVER. COME THROUGH THE PORTAL TO FIND A WORLD IN CHAOS.

ALLIES.

GINGERNINJA94

ENEMIES.

WAR.

BUILD YOUR RANK AND REPUTATION AS YOU FIGHT AGAINST OTHER PLAYERS AROUND THE WORLD.

RANKING UP!

COR, THE LEGENDARY GOLDEN AXE!

Power Level: 1000+

COMPETE IN THE CLASH ARENA FOR PVP GLORY! ONLY THE TOP RANKED PLAYERS GET THE BEST REWARDS.

-999!

THE PROBLEM IS, IF YOU DON'T KEEP WINNING, YOUR RANK CAN PLUMMET.

nooooooo my axe!!

Rank: DROPPED!

AND THOSE JUICY GOLDEN WEAPONS WILL BE OUT OF REACH FOREVER.

THERE WILL BE NO MORE FUN FOR YOU, MY APPRENTICE.

awwww...

FOR TODAY, YOU GO TO WORK.

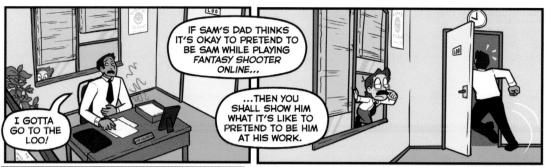

I GOTTA GO TO THE LOO!

IF SAM'S DAD THINKS IT'S OKAY TO PRETEND TO BE SAM WHILE PLAYING *FANTASY SHOOTER* ONLINE...

...THEN YOU SHALL SHOW HIM WHAT IT'S LIKE TO PRETEND TO BE HIM AT HIS WORK.

Tax Form 20-J

hmm yes business

me
business case

C-

FILE THESE BUSINESS PAPERS, PLEASE!

uhm...

LOOK AT THIS LINE! THIS LINE IS NO GOOD!

gasp!

Oh!

HE'S RIGHT!

SELL! SELL! SELL!

WOW!

SELLING NOW, SIR!

So good!

GREAT JOB TODAY! YOU'RE AN ASSET TO THE BUSINESS!

THANK YOU, SIR!

FLUSSHH!

OOPS! GOTTA GO.

YOU'VE ALREADY DONE ALL YOUR WORK, YOU CAN GO HOME EARLY!

SWEET! MORE TIME FOR GAMES!

WHILE I'VE BEEN WORKING ALL DAY, WERE YOU JUST PLAYING GAMES?

IF YOU CONSIDER THE MOST HARDCORE GAMING SESSION EVER TO BE 'PLAYING'...

ZAPOW! DING!

THEN, YEAH, I'VE BEEN *PLAYING.*

NOW, WHERE WAS I?

Fantasy SHOOTER online

KABOOOM!

WHOA!

WHO'S THIS?!

Character Select

Rank: MAXIMUM DADELUS653

HEY, SAM, CHECK OUT! MY OWN ACCOUNT!

AND HE'S AT MY RANK! AWESOME!

WANNA OWN NOOBS IN THE CLASH ARENA TOGETHER?

LET'S DO IT!

SOMETIMES JUSTICE IS SERVED, NOT BY PUNISHMENT, BUT BY GENEROSITY.

Pow! Zap! hahaha! yeah!

SPEAKING OF WHICH, I MADE A TON OF MONEY TODAY. WANNA GO BUY SOMETHING?

THAT WHICH I CARE ABOUT CANNOT BE BOUGHT OR SOLD. OF COURSE, I'M TALKING ABOUT...

IS IT JUSTICE

...JUSTICE.

JUSTICE SERVED

OPERATION FEE TO WEE

30p to use the loo?!

THE TRAIN IS NOW ARRIVING AT THE STATION.

BACK SO SOON, MY APPRENTICE?

THE LOO'S OUT OF ORDER!

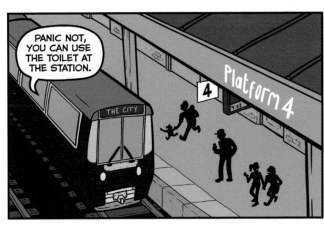

PANIC NOT, YOU CAN USE THE TOILET AT THE STATION.

THE CITY

Platform 4

4

TOILETS

30p CHARGE

WHAT IS THIS?!

THAT'LL BE 30p.

PAYING TO USE A TOILET?

I THINK I HAVE IT...!

30p CHARGE

TOILETS

30p CHARGE

DON'T YOU DARE!

YAWN...!

noooooo...!

30p CHARGE

30p FOR A WEE?! THIS INJUSTICE WILL NOT STAND!

DISGUISED AS *MYSELF*...

I, *CLAIRE*, JUSTICE NINJA: NINJA OF *JUSTICE*...

WILL BRING JUSTICE TO THE *PAY-TO-PEE* PROFITEERS!

LOOK AT THEM. LEMMINGS. *SHEEP!* PAYING TO USE THE TOILET!

WHO DO THEY THINK WE ARE?

TITANS OF INDUSTRY? OIL BILLIONAIRES? CORRUPT GOVERNMENT OFFICIALS?! WE WILL DEFEAT THE TYRANNY OF THE TOILET-PAYMENT SYSTEM!

IT'S JUST 30p!

I HOPE THE *P* STANDS FOR *PRINCIPLES!*

AND *MY* PRINCIPLES ARE NOT FOR SALE.

LOOK, CLAIRE, YOU'RE RIGHT! BUT I *REALLY* HAVE TO GO! CAN'T I JUST PAY THE 30p SO I CAN—

YOU'RE DESPERATE! THEY'RE TAKING ADVANTAGE OF YOU!

TIME TO PUT MY PLAN INTO ACTION. *TO THE MINISTRY FOR PUBLIC LOOS!*

I DON'T THINK THAT EXISTS, CLAIRE...!

JUSTICE SERVED

OPERATION STAND UP AND BAND UP

first years

NO bullies allowed!

St Martin's Primary School

HIYA, CLAIRE.

GOOD MORNING, HORACE.

Chomp.

YOU'D BETTER GET GOING. THE FIRST BELL'S GONNA *RING* ANY MINUTE.

THANKS FOR THE REMINDER.

WAIT, WHERE ARE YOU GOING?

TO THE LITTLE KID PLAYGROUND. I *FORGOT* MY LUNCH MONEY, SO I'LL TAKE IT FROM SOME SNOTTY-NOSED YEAR ONE.

LATERS.

LUNCH MONEY?! WHAT YOU NEED IS *JUSTICE!*

DISGUISED AS *MYSELF*, I, *CLAIRE*, JUSTICE NINJA: NINJA OF JUSTICE...

WILL BRING JUSTICE FOR THE *LITTLE KIDS AT SCHOOL!*

BULLYING IS *RIFE* AT OUR SCHOOL, NIGEL.

EXTORTION.

RACKETEERING.

INTIMIDATION.

I DON'T KNOW WHAT *ANY* OF THOSE WORDS MEAN.

THAT'S BECAUSE THE TEACHERS DON'T HAVE TIME TO TEACH WITH SO MANY *BULLIES* ON THE LOOSE!

AND THE KINGPIN: *HORACE MINEFIELD.*

A *NETWORK* OF BULLIES THE LIKES OF WHICH NO SCHOOL HAS *EVER* SEEN BEFORE!

SO HOW DO WE TAKE OUT HORACE?

WE PAY A VISIT TO THE *LITTLE KIDS.*

IT'S NOT *FAIR*. WHAT CHANCE DOES A YEAR ONE HAVE AGAINST HIM? HORACE IS *HUGE*!

THERE'S SOMETHING BIGGER THAN *ANY* BULLY, AND WE'LL SHOW THE LITTLE KIDS *PRECISELY* WHAT IT IS.

MY FAVOURITE COLOUR IS BLUE.

BLUE'S MY FAVOURITE TOO!

WANNA DRAW SOMETHING *TOGETHER*?

OKAY!

IT'S MINE!

NO, IT'S MINE!

WHAT IF WE *SHARE*?

FOR 2 PLAYERS

LET'S MAKE ONE *MASSIVE* BLOCK CASTLE TOGETHER!

YEAH!

little kids united

Woo!

Yeah!

VERY GOOD, TINY PEOPLE. YOU ARE BEGINNING TO SEE WHAT YOU CAN ACCOMPLISH WHEN YOU ACT AS *ONE*.

NEXT MORNING.

OFF TO THE LITTLE KID AREA FOR LUNCH MONEY?

YUP. GOTTA HAVE A HOBBY.

OH, BABIES...!

...HELLO?

YOU WANT LUNCH MONEY, HORACE?

YOU CAN HAVE *MINE!*

MINE *TOO!*

little kids united

YOU CAN HAVE *ALL* OF OUR LUNCH MONEYS...

BUT YOU'RE GONNA HAVE TO *TAKE* IT.

YOU MAY BE *BIG,* HORACE...

...BUT *TOGETHER,* WE'RE A LOT BIGGER!

MAKE A NOTE, MY APPRENTICE. THE TINY PEOPLE ARE A *POWERFUL* FORCE WHEN PROPERLY UTILISED IN THE SERVING OF *JUSTICE.*

OKAY. GREAT. CAN WE GET DOWN NOW? I *REALLY* DON'T LIKE HEIGHTS!

AAAAAAAAH!

CLAIRE? HELLO? WHERE'D YOU... OH, CRUMBS.

JUSTICE SERVED

60

Nigel's Tippest Tipper? super tips!
GUIDE TO FRIENDSHIP!!
best friends
SO WHAT DO YOU THINK? PRETTY GOOD, RIGHT?!
YOU STILL HAVE MUCH TO LEARN, MY APPRENTICE.